Name:

How to use t___ ____

The book is designed to use in personal Bible study, in small groups, or to accompany teaching sessions.

The aim is to enable you to grasp the story line or plot of the Bible by studying the key passages and reading the brief notes.

The checkboxes are provided so that you can tick them when you have read and thought about the Bible passages. There are often a lot of Bible passages and you may decide to study some of these alone, before or after a group session. It is important to give time to reading the passages and of course you may decide to read more than just the selected passages!

Tick the big checkbox at the end of each topic when you feel that you have completed the study and understand this section of the Bible.

There are 10 topics, each on a double page spread. You may manage to cover some of these topics in a single session or they might take longer.

I have written this book using the New International Version of the Bible but you should be able to use any other version.

I hope that Bible Plot will be helpful in enabling you to understand the Bible better.

John Robertshaw

"...and how from infancy you have known the holy Scriptures, which are able to make you wise for salvation through faith in Christ Jesus. All Scripture is God-breathed and is useful for teaching, rebuking, correcting and training in righteousness, so that the man of God may be thoroughly equipped for every good work. (2 Tim 3:15-17)

bible plot 1

● Abraham | ● Moses ● Samuel
● Isaac ● Joseph | ● Joshua
● Jacob = Israel
● Noah | Egypt | Judges
● Adam | Flood | Babel

? BC | 2000 BC | 1500 BC | 1000 BC
CREATION---FALL-----------JUDGMENT -----------PROMISE---------SLAVERY------LAW---LAND-----------

beginning

creation

☐ Gen 1:1-2:3

The six days can be divided into two sets of three:

Day 1   Light and darkness | Day 4   Sun, moon and stars
Day 2   Sky and water | Day 5   Birds and fish
Day 3   Dry land and vegetation | Day 6   Animals and humans

Day 7   God's sabbath day

before the beginning - eternity

God has existed always - he is "eternal" and without beginning or end. He was never created. He has always existed as the Father, the Son and the Holy Spirit. Angels were created before the material universe.

adam and eve

☐ Gen 2:4-3:24

Eve listened to the serpent and Adam listened to Eve. They broke the one command which God had given them. They tried to shift the blame and did not own up to their sin. They were expelled from the garden and life on earth became a struggle for them.

the image of God

Human beings are different from the rest of creation - they are made "in the image of God" and are given a special task to look after the earth. Biologically we are similar to animals, but spiritually we resemble God - as in our ability to communicate, to love, to appreciate beauty, to choose and to love God.

Biological	Spiritual
God	God
———	humans
humans	———
animals	animals
plants	plants
earth	earth

cain and abel

☐ Gen 4:1-26

Sin was carried through to the next generation. Cain was jealous, angry and deceitful and this led to hate and murder. He was evasive about his sin and there was no sign of repentance. Abel became the first martyr - a righteous man who died at the hands of the wicked.

the serpent

Rev 12:9 clearly identifies the ancient serpent as the devil or Satan.

The Bible suggests that the devil began as an angel who rebelled against God with other angels, who became demons.

David	Elijah	Isaiah	Jeremiah	Ezra		
Saul	Solomon	Ahab	Hezekiah	Ezekiel	Alexander the Great	Jesus
One Kingdom	"Israel" (North)		Daniel			Julius Caesar
	"Judah" (South)			"Jews"		

1000 BC	500 BC	BC - 0 - AD
----------KINGDOM------------------------------EXILE--RETURN--MESSIAH

noah

❑ Gen 6:1-9:17

Sin had now spread to the whole of the human race:

"every inclination of the thoughts of his heart was only evil all the time", "the earth was corrupt in God's sight and full of violence"

The flood was God's judgment. Noah, his family and the animals were saved in the ark.

God's covenant with humans and with all living creatures

After surviving the flood with his family, Noah built an altar and made a sacrifice to God as a way of giving thanks.

God makes a covenant which include the following promises:

• not to curse the ground again
• that the seasons will remain
• that humans may eat meat
• an accounting in blood
• that life will not be destroyed again in the same way

The sign of the covenant is the rainbow.

babel

❑ Gen 11:1-9

The flood did not solve the problems in the human heart. The city of Babel was a symbol of human pride in its own achievements. The tower would have been a religious building for worship of false gods. God's judgment upon them was confusion of languages.

Babel later became *Babylon* which, in the Bible, is the major symbol of the world's human, political and religious systems opposed to God. *Jerusalem,* on the other hand, is the city of God, representing his people and his kingdom.

spoilt image

When Adam and Eve sinned, the image of God in them was spoilt. This spoilt image became a feature of human nature. We are all sinners and under a sentence of death (Rom 5:12). Since Adam was in charge of the earth, this also became spoiled and human existence on the earth would be a struggle (Gen 3:17-19). This offers an explanation for the imperfections on the earth such as sickness, decay and disaster.

The remainder of the Bible story is about God's solution to these basic problems in human beings and the earth.

Yes!

I have read all the Bible passages.

I have thought about the issues and understand this unit.

3

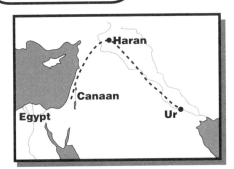
promise

abraham

☐ Gen 11:27-13:18
☐ Gen 15:1-18:15

God's covenant with abraham

The main promises are:

- Abraham would have many descendants who would become a great nation under the blessing and protection of God.
- Abraham would become the father of many nations and all the nations of the earth would be blessed through Abraham and his offspring.
- Abraham's descendants would possess the land of Canaan and the surrounding area.

These promises were made without conditions and were only to be received by faith. Circumcision was a sign of the covenant.

God's blessing

Abraham

↓

a great nation (Israel)

↓

offspring (Jesus)

↓

all nations of the world

Abraham was born in the heathen city of Ur but moved north with his family to Haran. When Abraham was 75, God spoke to him and guided him to the land of Canaan. God made a covenant with Abraham including a promise of children and of possession of land.

When Abraham did not have children with his wife Sarah, his patience ran out and he tried to do God's will his own way. He slept with Sarah's maid and she had a son called Ishmael. This was not God's plan. Ishmael became the father of the Arab nations. God, however, still had plans for Sarah.

☐ **Gen 21:1-21** ☐ **Gen 22:1-19** ☐ **Gen 25:7-11**

Sarah gave birth to a son at the age of 90. This was so amusing that they called him Isaac which means "laughter".

☐ **Rom 4:1-25** Abraham is the spiritual father of all who believe the promises of God.

☐ **Gal 3:6-16** Jesus is the offspring who brings the blessing to the gentiles.

☐ **Heb 11:8-19** Abraham is the man of faith. He believed God against all the odds.

● David   ● Elijah ● Isaiah ● Jeremiah ● Ezra
● Saul ● Solomon ● Ahab ● Hezekiah   ● Ezekiel   ● Alexander the Great   ● Jesus

One Kingdom	"Israel" (North)			● Daniel		● Julius Caesar
	"Judah" (South)			"Jews"		

1000 BC   500 BC   BC - 0 - AD

----------KINGDOM--------------------------EXILE--RETURN--MESSIAH

isaac, jacob and esau

❑ **Gen 24:1-67**   ❑ **Gen 25:19-34**   ❑ **Gen 27:1-40**

Abraham's servant went to Haran to find a wife for Isaac who then married Rebekah. They had twins, Jacob and Esau. Jacob was the youngest son but he cheated his brother and got the birthright and the blessing.

❑ **Gen 27:41-31:21**

As Jacob escaped from Esau, he had a revelation from God through a dream and made a vow. Jacob worked for his uncle Laban for many years, married both his daughters, Rachel and Leah, and had children by them and by their maids.

❑ **Gen 35:1-29**

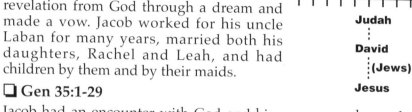

Jacob had an encounter with God and his name was changed to *Israel*. The families of his twelve sons became *the twelve tribes of Israel*.

joseph

❑ **Gen 37:1-36**   ❑ **Gen 39:1-47:31**

Israel's favourite son, Joseph, was sold into slavery by his jealous brothers. But God had his hand on the situation and Joseph became a ruler in Egypt. The whole family moved to Egypt.

prophecy

❑ **Gen 48:1-50:26** Israel prophesied over his children. Read about Judah in Gen 49:8-12. The King will come from Judah!

summary

❑ **Acts 7:1-16**   Read this summary.

Yes!

I have read all the Bible passages.

I have thought about the issues and understand this unit.

5

bible plot 3

● Abraham
● Isaac ● Joseph
● Jacob = Israel

● Noah

● Adam   **Flood**   **Babel**   **Egypt**

● Moses ● Samuel
● Joshua

Judges

? BC   2000 BC   1500 BC   1000 BC
CREATION---FALL------------JUDGMENT ----------PROMISE--------SLAVERY-----LAW--LAND------------

moses

egypt to sinai

❏ Ex 1:1-19:25

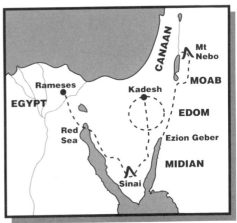

Over 400 years in Egypt, Israel's family increased from seventy to many thousands and the Egyptians set them to work as slaves. God called Moses to set them free to return to Canaan. After a number of plagues, culminating in the death of the first-born in Egypt, Pharaoh agreed to their departure. God worked further miracles, dividing the Red Sea, providing food and water, and defeating the Amalekites. They arrived at Mount Sinai and God revealed himself to the people.

passover

The Jews still celebrate the passover each year as they remember deliverance by the blood of a lamb.

Jesus used this ceremony to point to his own blood which would save the world.

the law of moses

The law of Moses is spread through the books of Exodus, Leviticus, Numbers and Deuteronomy. It includes laws relating to:

• **Community life** - how to live together as a community on the move and in the promised land
• **Justice** - how to deal with those who break God's laws
• **Food** - what food should be eaten
• **Hygiene** - dealing with infectious diseases and sources of infection
• **Marriage and divorce**
• **Family life** - maintaining healthy family life
• **Sex** - what behaviour is permitted
• **True worship** - avoidance of idolatry, false religion and the occult
• **Sabbaths and special feasts**
• **Worship of God** - at the tabernacle or temple
• **Priests and sacrifices**
• **Taking the land of Canaan**

the law

❏ Ex 20:1-21

God spoke the *ten commandments* to the people. Later God wrote these on tablets of stone.

❏ Ex 20:22-24:18

Moses went up the mountain and God gave him many more laws and a *covenant* was made by a meal, the reading of the law and sacrifices.

God also gave Moses the design of the *tabernacle*.

6

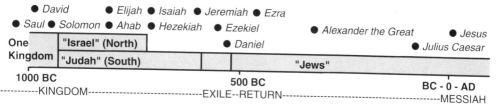

golden calf

☐ Ex 32:1-34:35

Even while Moses was listening to God, the people turned to idolatry and other sin. Moses intercedes for the people and returns to the mountain and has an amazing revelation of God and his covenant.

tabernacle

☐ Ex 35:4-40:38

The people spent some time making the tabernacle according to God's plan. It was a portable temple to be used for sacrifices and for meeting with God.

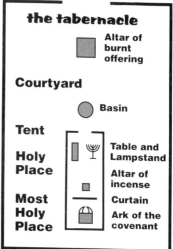

the tabernacle

Altar of burnt offering

Courtyard

Basin

Tent

Holy Place — Table and Lampstand, Altar of incense

Most Holy Place — Curtain, Ark of the covenant

moses covenant

The Moses covenant involved the passover, the exodus and the giving of the law.

We read about the blood of the covenant (sacrifices), the book of the covenant (law), the tablets of the covenant (10 commandments), the ark of the covenant (presence of God). Signs of the covenant include the passover and the keeping of the sabbath.

It was a conditional covenant. Obedience brought blessings and disobedience brought curses.

☐ Lev 16:1-34   ☐ Heb 9:1-10:18

The tabernacle, the priest and the sacrifices were a shadow of the new covenant where Jesus is the high priest and the sacrifice.

rebellion

☐ Num 11:1-14:45 ☐ Num 20:1-13
☐ Num 16:1-17:13 ☐ Num 21:4-9

Because the Israelites were rebellious, they wandered around the desert for forty years so that a whole generation died before they entered the promised land.

summary

☐ Deut 1:1-3:29   ☐ Deut 28:1-68
☐ Deut 34:1-12
☐ Acts 7:17-45   ☐ Heb 11:23-29

Moses sees the land before he dies.

Yes!

I have read all the Bible passages.

I have thought about the issues and understand this unit.

bible plot 4

● Adam   ● Noah   Flood   Babel   ● Abraham   ● Isaac   ● Joseph   ● Jacob = Israel   Egypt   ● Moses   ● Joshua   Judges   ● Samuel

? BC .... 2000 BC .... 1500 BC .... 1000 BC
CREATION---FALL------------JUDGMENT ----------PROMISE--------SLAVERY------LAW---LAND-------------

the land

entering the land

☐ **Joshua 1:1-8:35**

God miraculously stopped the River Jordan, enabling the Israelites to cross to Gilgal. They then followed God's unusual strategy to take the first objective, Jericho. After a temporary set-back and defeat at Ai, they proceeded to Mount Ebal to build an altar and to confirm their covenant with God.

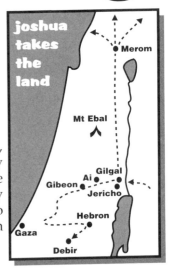

joshua takes the land

canaanites

The land of Canaan was occupied by a selection of tribes including the Hittites, Girgashites, Amorites, Canaanites, Perizzites, Hivites and Jebusites. Sometimes they are all described as Canaanites or Amorites.

These people were very sinful - see Lev 18:1-20:27 for a catalogue of sins which were practiced in the land and which the Israelites should avoid.

The conquest of Canaan by Joshua was God's judgment on these wicked people which was prophesied over 400 years before (Gen 15:12-16, Deut 9:4-5).

taking the land

☐ **Joshua 9:1-11:23**

The victory at Gibeon in the south and Merom in the north opened the way for Joshua to take many more cities in the land.

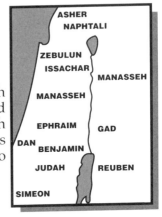

occupying the land

The tribes of Israel settled in the land. Manasseh and Ephraim, the sons of Joseph, were counted as full tribes. Manasseh had territory on both sides of the Jordan. The tribe of Levi was devoted to the service of the Lord and had no land area but lived in special cities.

☐ **Joshua 23:1-24:33** Read this summary.

8

● David ● Elijah ● Isaiah ● Jeremiah ● Ezra
● Saul ● Solomon ● Ahab ● Hezekiah ● Ezekiel ● Alexander the Great ● Jesus

One Kingdom | "Israel" (North) | ● Daniel | ● Julius Caesar | ● Jesus
"Judah" (South) | "Jews"

1000 BC ---------- **500 BC** ---------- **BC - 0 - AD**
----------KINGDOM----------------------------EXILE--RETURN--MESSIAH

defending the land

☐ **Judges 1:1-3:6**

The Israelites did not manage to remove the Canaanites from the land and they remained as "thorns in their sides". The Israelites were tempted to intermarry and worship the gods of these people. As well as the Canaanites, they were surrounded by unfriendly nations who attacked them. God raised up judges to rescue them.

☐ **Judges 4:1-24** Deborah and the Canaanites

☐ **Judges 6:1-7:25** Gideon and the Midianites

☐ **Judges 13:1-16:31** Samson and the Philistines

Judges
- Othniel
- Ehud
- Shamgar
- Deborah
- Gideon
- Tola
- Jair
- Jephthah
- Ibzan
- Elon
- Abdon
- Samson
- (Samuel)

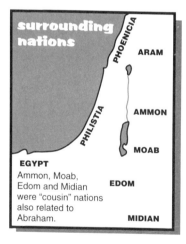

surrounding nations

PHOENICIA
ARAM
PHILISTIA
AMMON
MOAB
EGYPT
EDOM
MIDIAN

Ammon, Moab, Edom and Midian were "cousin" nations also related to Abraham.

samuel

☐ **1 Samuel 1:1-3:21**

God heard the prayer of Hannah and she became the mother of Samuel. As a boy, he had a clear call from God and was the last judge of Israel.

give us a king

☐ **1 Samuel 7:15-10:27**

The people wanted a king so that they could be like the nations around them. One of Samuel's main tasks was to appoint and anoint the first king of Israel - Saul.

Yes!

I have read all the Bible passages.

I have thought about the issues and understand this unit.

9

bible plot 5

● Abraham ● Moses ● Samuel
● Isaac ● Joseph ● Joshua
● Noah ● Jacob = Israel
● Adam **Flood** **Babel** **Egypt** | **Judges**

| ? BC | 2000 BC | 1500 BC | 1000 BC |

CREATION---FALL-------------JUDGMENT ----------PROMISE--------SLAVERY------LAW---LAND-------------

kingdom

saul

❏ **1 Sam 13:1-15**   ❏ **1 Sam 14:47-48**   ❏ **1 Sam 15:1-35**

Saul proved to be a good fighter and his army subdued the surrounding nations. He was, however, impatient, arrogant and rebellious and God rejected him and his family as kings of Israel. He became increasingly insecure, defensive and obsessive about destroying David. He and his son Jonathan came to a sad end. Surprisingly Saul reigned over Israel for over 40 years!

david

❏ **1 Sam 16:1-19:24**   ❏ **1 Sam 24:1-22**

❏ **1 Sam 26:1-27:12**   ❏ **1 Sam 31:1-13**

❏ **2 Sam 2:1-7**   ❏ **2 Sam 5:1- 8:18**

❏ **2 Sam 11:1-12:25**   ❏ **2 Sam 22:1-23:7**

❏ **1 Chron 22:1-19**   ❏ **1 Chron 28:1-21**

After years running away from Saul, David became king - first over the tribe of Judah and then over all Israel. He subdued the surrounding nations, established the kingdom of Israel with the capital at Jerusalem and God made a covenant with him. His sin with Bathsheba involved adultery, treachery and murder and was the beginning of problems in his family and other areas.

david's life

age	Shepherd boy in Bethlehem
	Musician to Saul
	Anointed by Samuel
	Defeated Goliath
	Attacked by Saul
	On the run from Saul
	Gathered a small army
	Lived among the Philistines
	Saul and Jonathan died
30	Became king over Judah
	Ruled in Hebron
37	Became king over all Israel.
	Made Jerusalem his base
	Built a palace
	Brought Ark to Jerusalem
	God's covenant with David
	Defeated nearby nations
	Expanded the kingdom
	Sin with Bathsheba
	Family problems
	Absalom's rebellion
	Military census
	Organised temple worship
	Preparations for the temple
	Adonijah's rebellion
	Solomon appointed king
70	Death of David

● David ● Elijah ● Isaiah ● Jeremiah ● Ezra
● Saul ● Solomon ● Ahab ● Hezekiah ● Ezekiel · ● Alexander the Great · · · · · · · ● Jesus

| One Kingdom | "Israel" (North) | | ● Daniel | | ● Julius Caesar |

One Kingdom | "Israel" (North) | | ● Daniel
| "Judah" (South) | | "Jews" |

1000 BC   500 BC   BC - 0 - AD
--------KINGDOM----------------------------EXILE--RETURN--MESSIAH

psalms

David was a poet and musician who composed nearly half of the book of psalms. These songs relate to his relationship with God, his experiences of life, his prayers and his prophetic gifting. Many people are encouraged as they read or sing psalms.

Help in trouble	❏ Ps 17	❏ Ps 55
Repentance	❏ Ps 32	❏ Ps 51
Thanks	❏ Ps 21	❏ Ps 30
Praise	❏ Ps 19	❏ Ps 103
Protection	❏ Ps 23	❏ Ps 27

david covenant

2 Sam 7 - David wanted to build a temple. God did not allow this but instead made a covenant with David:

- David's name would be great.
- There would be peace and security for the people of Israel in the land God had given them.
- David's son would build a temple.
- David's family would continue to sit on the throne of Israel and the kingdom would endure for ever!

It was because of these promises that the people of Israel expected a king (a Messiah) to come from the "line of David" and to establish the kingdom. The New Testament identifies Jesus as this son of David who will reign as king for ever over an everlasting kingdom (Luke 1:29-33).

solomon

❏ 1 Kings 3:1-11:43

Solomon built on the successes of David. He adopted a lavish and splendid lifestyle and built the magnificent temple that David had designed, which was like a large version of the tabernacle. He had some impressive encounters with God in his earlier years but unfortunately his many wives and carelessness in later life resulted in God's judgment upon him and his family.

solomon's writings

Song of Songs - Probably written when Solomon was young. This is a poem about the love between a man and a woman.

Proverbs - This is a collection of wise sayings and advice for living. There is encouragement to gain wisdom and to avoid folly.

Ecclesiastes - Probably written in Solomon's old age. It is a rather cynical view of the futility of life here on earth.

❏ SS 1-2   ❏ Prov 1-4   ❏ Eccl 1-3

Yes!

I have read all the Bible passages.

I have thought about the issues and understand this unit.

bible plot 6

● Abraham   ● Moses ● Samuel
● Isaac ● Joseph   ● Joshua
● Noah   ● Jacob = Israel
● Adam   Flood   Babel   Egypt   Judges

? BC   2000 BC   1500 BC   1000 BC
CREATION---FALL------------JUDGMENT ----------PROMISE--------SLAVERY------LAW---LAND-------------

judah & israel

the kingdom divides

❑ 1 Kings 12:1-19

Solomon's son unwisely took bad advice and the Kingdom divided into two. Ten tribes formed the Northern kingdom of "Israel" with its capital at Samaria with King Jeroboam. The tribes of Judah and Benjamin formed the Southern kingdom of "Judah" with its capital at Jerusalem with King Rehoboam.

israel (north)

❑ 1 Kings 12:25-33   ❑ 1 Kings 16:29-19:21   ❑ 2 Kings 2:1-6:23
❑ Amos 5:1-27   ❑ Hosea 8:1-14   ❑ 2 Kings 17:1-41

Israel had a series of wicked kings and engaged in all manner of sin and false religion. Despite warnings from Elijah, Elisha and other prophets, they did not change their ways. Eventually the Assyrians invaded and deported most of the population.

words

The word "Israel" can refer to the man, Jacob, all the 12 tribes, or the northern kingdom of 10 tribes.

The northern kingdom of Israel is sometimes referred to as "Jacob", "Ephraim", or "Joseph".

"Zion" is another word for Jerusalem. The city, the people of Judah or the whole of the Israelites are called the "daughter of Zion".

judah (south)

❑ 2 Chron 12:1-16:14   ❑ 2 Chron 20:1-21:20
❑ 2 Chron 29:1-36:23   ❑ Jer 25:1-14
❑ Jer 29:1-14   ❑ Mic 1:1-7:20   ❑ Zeph 1:1-3:20

Judah had some very good kings and some wicked kings. Under King Hezekiah they escaped being taken by the Assyrians. However, eventually, they were conquered by the Babylonians and the population deported to Babylon. Jeremiah prophesied that they would spend 70 years in exile in Babylon.

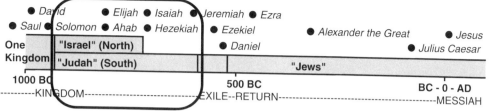

Timeline (top):
- David ● Elijah ● Isaiah ● Jeremiah ● Ezra
- Saul ● Solomon ● Ahab ● Hezekiah ● Ezekiel ● Alexander the Great ● Jesus
- Daniel ● Julius Caesar
- One Kingdom | "Israel" (North) | "Judah" (South) | "Jews"
- 1000 BC ——————— 500 BC ——————— BC - 0 - AD
- ----------KINGDOM---------------------------EXILE--RETURN-----------------------------------MESSIAH

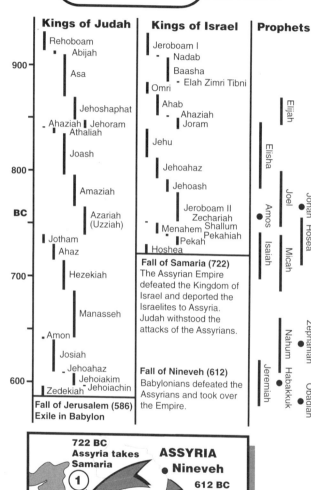

Kings of Judah	Kings of Israel	Prophets
		the prophets

Kings of Judah

- Rehoboam
- Abijah
- 900
- Asa
- Jehoshaphat
- Ahaziah — Jehoram — Athaliah
- Joash
- 800
- Amaziah
- Azariah (Uzziah)
- BC
- Jotham
- Ahaz
- 700
- Hezekiah
- Manasseh
- Amon
- Josiah
- Jehoahaz
- Jehoiakim — Jehoiachin
- 600
- Zedekiah

Fall of Jerusalem (586)
Exile in Babylon

Kings of Israel

- Jeroboam I
- Nadab
- Baasha
- Elah Zimri Tibni
- Omri
- Ahab
- Ahaziah — Joram
- Jehu
- Jehoahaz
- Jehoash
- Jeroboam II
- Zechariah
- Menahem — Shallum — Pekahiah
- Pekah
- Hoshea

Fall of Samaria (722)
The Assyrian Empire defeated the Kingdom of Israel and deported the Israelites to Assyria. Judah withstood the attacks of the Assyrians.

Fall of Nineveh (612)
Babylonians defeated the Assyrians and took over the Empire.

Prophets
- Elijah
- Elisha
- Amos
- Joel
- Jonah
- Hosea
- Isaiah
- Micah
- Zephaniah
- Nahum
- Habakkuk
- Obadiah
- Jeremiah

the prophets

Elijah and Elisha were "charismatic" prophets who performed miracles and confronted political leaders.

Jonah and Nahum prophesied to Nineveh, capital of the Assyrian Empire. The people of Nineveh repented after hearing Jonah. Nineveh fell shortly after the prophecy of Nahum.

Joel used a plague of locusts to warn Judah and other nations about God's judgment. He predicted a future pouring out of God's Spirit.

Amos and Hosea exposed the sins of Israel and warned of God's judgment upon them and defeat by the Assyrians.

Isaiah and Micah prophesied judgment on Israel, Judah and many other nations. They also spoke about the future restoration of Israel, the coming Messiah, salvation, and the establishment of God's kingdom.

Zephaniah predicted judgment on Judah and the future restoration of all Israel.

Jeremiah called Judah to repent and return to God. He prophesied defeat by the Babylonians and a 70 year exile for Judah.

Habakkuk discussed with God about the judgment on nations and God's ultimate purposes.

Obadiah prophesied judgment on Edom (Esau's descendants).

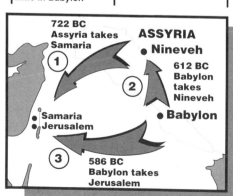

722 BC Assyria takes Samaria (1)
ASSYRIA ● Nineveh
612 BC Babylon takes Nineveh (2)
● Samaria ● Jerusalem
● Babylon
586 BC Babylon takes Jerusalem (3)

Yes!
I have read all the Bible passages.

I have thought about the issues and understand this unit.

13

bible plot 7

			Abraham Isaac ● Joseph	Moses ● Samuel
		Noah	Jacob = Israel	Joshua
Adam	Flood	Babel	Egypt	Judges

| ? BC | 2000 BC | 1500 BC | 1000 BC |
| CREATION---FALL-----------JUDGMENT ----------PROMISE---------SLAVERY------LAW---LAND------------- |

exile & return

life in exile

☐ **Jer 52:28-30** ☐ **Psalm 137** Nebuchadnezzar took the most intelligent and qualified people from Judah to Babylon. They settled there but longed to return to their own land, city, temple and God.

☐ **Dan 1:1-4:37** Daniel became an advisor to Nebuchadnezzar and his friends resisted the pressure to serve other Gods.

☐ **Ezek 37:1-27** Ezekiel encouraged the exiles.

☐ **Jer 52:31-34** Evil-Merodach released King Jehoiachin.

☐ **Dan 5:1-31** Babylon defeated by the Medes and Persians. Cyrus was King of Persia, Darius the Mede ruled over the province of Babylon.

☐ **Dan 6:1-28** Daniel thrown to the lions by Darius the Mede.

☐ **Esther 1:1-10:3** Esther became Queen of Persia.

"jews"

The people of Israel were first called "Jews" (from the word Judah) during this period of exile.

They also began to gather together in small groups to read the law - this was the beginning of what later became the synagogue.

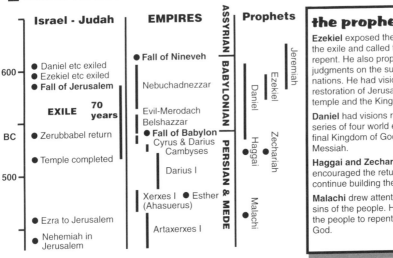

the prophets

Ezekiel exposed the reasons for the exile and called the people to repent. He also prophesied judgments on the surrounding nations. He had visions of restoration of Jerusalem, the temple and the Kingdom.

Daniel had visions relating to a series of four world empires, the final Kingdom of God and the Messiah.

Haggai and Zechariah encouraged the returning exiles to continue building the temple.

Malachi drew attention to various sins of the people. He encouraged the people to repent and return to God.

One Kingdom	"Israel" (North)			
	"Judah" (South)		"Jews"	

• David • Elijah • Isaiah • Jeremiah • Ezra
• Saul • Solomon • Ahab • Hezekiah • Ezekiel   • Alexander the Great • Jesus
  • Daniel   • Julius Caesar

1000 BC   500 BC   BC - 0 - AD
----------KINGDOM----------------------EXILE--RETURN----------------------------------MESSIAH

temple rebuilt - zerubbabel

☐ Isaiah 44:24-45:13   ☐ Dan 9:1-19

☐ Ezra 1:1-4

In line with the prophecies of Jeremiah and Isaiah and the prayer of Daniel, Cyrus decreed that Jews should return to Jerusalem and rebuild the temple.

☐ Ezra 1:5-4:5   ☐ Hag 1:1-15

☐ Zech 1:1-6   ☐ Zech 6:9-15

☐ Ezra 6:13-22

The temple was built with encouragement from Haggai and Zechariah.

law restored - ezra

☐ Ezra 7:1-10   ☐ Ezra 8:1-36

☐ Ezra 9:1-10:4   ☐ Neh 8:1-9:3

Ezra returned to Jerusalem with more exiles. He read the law and called the people to turn away from their sins.

walls repaired - nehemiah

☐ Neh 1:1-2:20   ☐ Neh 6:15-7:3

☐ Neh 12:27-47

Nehemiah repaired the walls of Jerusalem under substantial opposition.

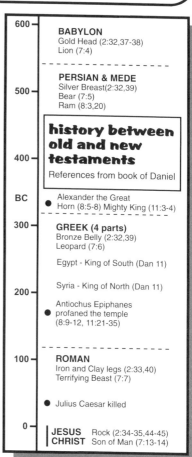

600 —

BABYLON
Gold Head (2:32,37-38)
Lion (7:4)

- - - - - - - - - - - - - - -

PERSIAN & MEDE
Silver Breast(2:32,39)
Bear (7:5)
Ram (8:3,20)

500 —

history between old and new testaments

References from book of Daniel

BC

Alexander the Great
Horn (8:5-8) Mighty King (11:3-4)

- - - - - - - - - - - - - - -

300 —

GREEK (4 parts)
Bronze Belly (2:32,39)
Leopard (7:6)

Egypt - King of South (Dan 11)

Syria - King of North (Dan 11)

200 —

Antiochus Epiphanes
profaned the temple
(8:9-12, 11:21-35)

- - - - - - - - - - - - - - -

100 —

ROMAN
Iron and Clay legs (2:33,40)
Terrifying Beast (7:7)

Julius Caesar killed

0 —

JESUS CHRIST Rock (2:34-35,44-45)
Son of Man (7:13-14)

Yes!

I have read all the Bible passages.

I have thought about the issues and understand this unit.

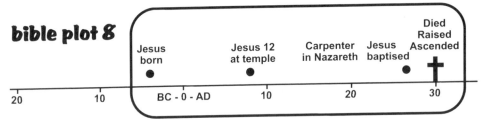

bible plot 8

Jesus born • | Jesus 12 at temple • | Carpenter in Nazareth | Jesus baptised • | Died Raised Ascended ✝

| 20 | 10 | BC - 0 - AD | 10 | 20 | 30 |

birth & early life

☐ Lk 1:1-2:21   ☐ Mt 1:18-2:23

☐ Lk 1:41-52

Jesus was born in Bethlehem. The family escaped to Egypt for a while and then settled in Nazareth, where Jesus became a carpenter.

Map of the region:
Tyre
Capernaum • Bethsaida •
GALILEE
Nazareth •   Gadara •
Caesarea •
DECAPOLIS
SAMARIA
Sychar •
PEREA
JUDEA   Jericho •
Jerusalem •
Bethany •
Bethlehem •

start of ministry

☐ Lk 3:1-4:30

At about 30, Jesus was baptised by John before being tempted in the desert for 40 days. He returned to Nazareth and announced his mission.

events in galilee - the north

☐ Jn 2:1-11   ☐ Jn 4:43-54   ☐ Lk 4:31-6:16   ☐ Mk 4:35-6:56

Jesus called and trained his disciples and performed many miracles in the north of Israel around the Sea of Galilee.

events in judea - the south

☐ Jn 5:1-15   ☐ Jn 8:1-11   ☐ Jn 9:1-41   ☐ Lk 10:38-42

☐ Jn 11:1-12:11   ☐ Lk 19:1-10

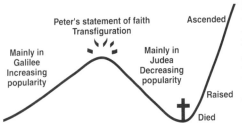

Peter's statement of faith
Transfiguration

Mainly in Galilee Increasing popularity

Mainly in Judea Decreasing popularity

Ascended

Raised

Died

Jesus went to Jerusalem for the regular Jewish feasts and used the opportunities to teach and heal. He spent more time in the south towards the end of his life. He became increasingly unpopular.

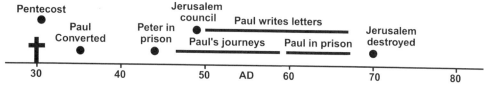

Pentecost — Paul Converted — Peter in prison — Jerusalem council — Paul writes letters — Paul's journeys — Paul in prison — Jerusalem destroyed

30   40   50   AD   60   70   80

his teaching

- ❏ Mt 5:1-7:29
- ❏ Mt 13:1-58
- ❏ Mt 18:1-20:28
- ❏ Lk 10:25-37
- ❏ Lk 14:25-18:14
- ❏ Jn 3:1-21
- ❏ Jn 7:1-52
- ❏ Jn 10:1-21

Jesus often used parables. He taught about how we should live and how we should relate to other people and to God. He taught about God's Kingdom and his own identity and role in our salvation.

turning point

- ❏ Jn 6:25-71
- ❏ Mt 16:13-17:13

Peter's confession of faith and the transfiguration marked a turning point in the ministry of Jesus. His popularity was fading, he set his face to Jerusalem and talked about his suffering.

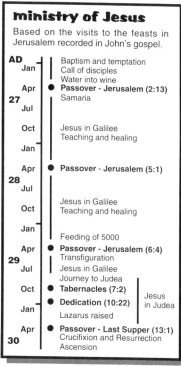

ministry of Jesus

Based on the visits to the feasts in Jerusalem recorded in John's gospel.

AD		
Jan		Baptism and temptation
		Call of disciples
		Water into wine
Apr	●	Passover - Jerusalem (2:13)
27		Samaria
Jul		
Oct		Jesus in Galilee
		Teaching and healing
Jan		
Apr	●	Passover - Jerusalem (5:1)
28		
Jul		
		Jesus in Galilee
Oct		Teaching and healing
Jan		
		Feeding of 5000
Apr	●	Passover - Jerusalem (6:4)
29		Transfiguration
Jul		Jesus in Galilee
		Journey to Judea
Oct	●	Tabernacles (7:2)
	●	Dedication (10:22) — Jesus in Judea
Jan		Lazarus raised
Apr	●	Passover - Last Supper (13:1)
30		Crucifixion and Resurrection
		Ascension

the last week - jesus died

- ❏ Mt 21:1-26:16
- ❏ Jn 13:1-14:30
- ❏ Lk 22:1-23:56

After a triumphant entry into Jerusalem on Sunday, Jesus spent the next few days teaching in the temple and engaging the religious leaders. On Thursday, he ate a final meal with his disciples before being arrested, tried and flogged during the night. He was nailed to the cross on Friday morning and died in the afternoon.

jesus alive again

- ❏ Jn 20:1-21:25
- ❏ Lk 24:1-53

Jesus was raised on Sunday and promised to send the Holy Spirit before ascending.

Yes!

I have read all the Bible passages.

I have thought about the issues and understand this unit.

17

bible plot 9

20   10   BC - 0 - AD   10   20   30

good news

the holy spirit

❏ Acts 1:1-2:47

Jesus sent the Holy Spirit to his disciples as promised on the day of pentecost and many people responded to the preaching of the gospel. The church developed as a community, meeting in homes and public places.

the promise fulfilled

Jesus is the saviour of the world and the book of Acts traces the spread of the gospel from the Jews in Jerusalem to Jews and Gentiles in many other countries.

The promise to Abraham is fulfilled - he becomes the father of many nations as people throughout the world come to faith in Jesus.

The everlasting Kingdom of God is growing as people submit to David's greater son - the King of Kings!

peter and john

❏ Acts 3:1-5:42   ❏ Acts 9:32-11:18   ❏ Acts 12:1-19

Peter and John continued the work of Jesus. They boldly proclaimed the good news of Jesus, confronted the religious leaders, healed the sick and delivered people from demons. They heard God's voice, saw angels and visions and were miraculously released from prison. God showed Peter that the good news was not just for the Jews but for the Gentiles too.

stephen and philip

❏ Acts 6:1-8:40

Others apart from the twelve apostles were also filled with the Holy Spirit, preached and saw miracles. Stephen became the first Christian martyr. Philip preached powerfully in Samaria with many signs and wonders. He also saw an African come to faith in Jesus.

conversion of saul (paul)

❏ Acts 9:1-31   ❏ Acts 11:19-30   ❏ Gal 1:11-2:10

Saul was a Jew from Tarsus who persecuted Christians. He was miraculously converted and became a powerful witness for Jesus with a special call to reach the Gentiles. It took time for the other believers to accept him. Eventually he moved to Antioch with Barnabas.

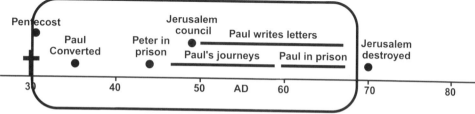

- ☐ Acts 13:1-15:35   1st journey
- ☐ Acts 15:36-18:22 2nd journey
- ☐ Acts 18:23-21:16 3rd journey
- ☐ Acts 21:17-28:31 in prison

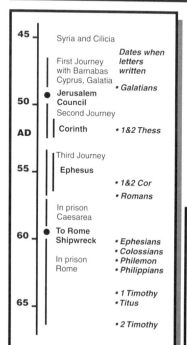

		Dates when letters written
45	Syria and Cilicia	
	First Journey with Barnabas Cyprus, Galatia	• Galatians
50	Jerusalem Council	
	Second Journey	
AD	Corinth	• 1&2 Thess
55	Third Journey	
	Ephesus	
		• 1&2 Cor
		• Romans
	In prison Caesarea	
60	To Rome Shipwreck	• Ephesians • Colossians • Philemon • Philippians
	In prison Rome	
		• 1 Timothy • Titus
65		• 2 Timothy

paul's journeys

After Paul's first journey around Galatia, he reported back to the church in Jerusalem that the Gentiles were receiving the gospel. The apostles and other leaders decided how Gentiles should respond to the Jewish laws (Acts 15).

Paul's further journeys took him to Greece. He spent time in Corinth and Ephesus. Eventually he was arrested, imprisoned and transferred to Rome.

letters

In the Bible we have many letters from Paul to churches he founded and to his helpers. He wrote to encourage, to teach, to correct and to advise.

We also have some letters from Peter, John and James.

Yes!

I have read all the Bible passages.

I have thought about the issues and understand this unit.

19

bible plot 10

Prophecies regarding the Messiah

Flood
Babel
Creation
Abraham Moses David Isaiah
Daniel
Babylon
Antiochus
Epiphanes
JESUS
CHRIST

prophecy

old testament

Most of the prophecies in the Old Testament are warnings and advice to the people of Judah, Israel and the other nations. The following elements are common:

Exposure of specific sins	❑ Isaiah 1:1-24
Warnings of judgment	❑ Isaiah 2:6-3:26
Call to repent and turn to God	❑ Isaiah 31:6
Promise of restoration	❑ Isaiah 35:1-10

Prophecies are complex. They are often not very logical but more like a collage of ideas woven together using words and imagery. Sometimes they will talk about events in the near future and the distant future in the same breath and often the actual words can refer to different events at the same time.

messianic prophecies

There are many prophecies referring to the coming of the Jesus:

His birth	❑ Micah 5:2 ❑ Is 7:14 ❑ Is 9:6-7
John the Baptist	❑ Isaiah 40:3-5 ❑ Malachi 3:1
Filled with Spirit	❑ Isaiah 11:1-5 ❑ Isaiah 61:1-3
Prophet, Priest, King	❑ Deut 18:17-19 ❑ Ps 110:1-4 ❑ Ps 2:1-12
Teaching and healing	❑ Psalm 78:1-2 ❑ Isaiah 42:7, 53:4
Entry into Jerusalem	❑ Zechariah 9:9
Betrayed	❑ Psalm 41:9 ❑ Zech 11:12-13
Suffering	❑ Ps 22:1-24 ❑ Is 53:1-12 ❑ Zech 12:10-11
Will not remain dead	❑ Psalm 16:10-11

20

Signs of
the end
Preaching
of the
gospel

JESUS
CHRIST

Great
Distress

Antichrist
End time Babylon

Armageddon

JESUS
CHRIST
RETURNS

Resurrection
of the saved

1000
years

Satan
destroyed

Final battle

Resurrection
and judgment
of the lost

New
heaven
New
earth

New
Jerusalem

end time prophecy

❏ Matthew 24:3-14 ❏ Revelation 6:1-17

After the first coming of Jesus there are signs of the end, persecution of Christians and the preaching of the gospel message.

❏ Matthew 24:15-25 ❏ Revelation 8:1-9:21

Nearer the end will come a time of great distress associated with the rule of the antichrist.

❏ Rev 13:11-18:24 ❏ 1 John 2:18-23

❏ 1 John 4:3 ❏ 2 John 7 ❏ Dan 8:9-12

❏ Dan 8:23-25 ❏ Dan 9:26-27 ❏ Dan 11:21-39

The antichrist will be opposed to God and will try to break the will of believers. His kingdom goes back to Babel and Babylon and is characterised by ungodliness, blasphemy, immorality, false religion, materialism and control. The ruler was prefigured by Antiochus Epiphanes described in Daniel.

❏ Rev 19:1-21 ❏ 2 Thess 2:1-12 ❏ Dan 7:8-14 ❏ Dan 7:23-27

❏ Matt 24:26-44 ❏ 1 Thess 4:13-18 ❏ Acts 1:9-11

Jesus will return as King of Kings and Lord of Lords, the end-time Babylon will be destroyed and the saved will be raised from the dead.

❏ Rev 20:1-15 ❏ John 5:28-29 ❏ 1 Cor 15:50-57

❏ Dan 12:2-3 ❏ 1 Cor 15:20-28 ❏ 2 Peter 3:1-14

Jesus will reign for 1000 years on earth before the final battle, the destruction of Satan and the resurrection and judgment of the lost.

❏ Rev 21:1-22:21 ❏ Is 65:17-25

The everlasting kingdom is described as the new Jerusalem. "The dwelling of God is with men and he will live with them."

end time

There are many interpretations of this prophetic information. The description is given here to help you to read the parts of the Bible and tie the information together.

application

The main application of these prophecies is to encourage us all to watch, pray and be ready for the return of our Lord Jesus. Persecution may come and we must stand firm to the end.

conclusion

Jesus is the winner!

Evil will be destroyed and every tongue will confess that Jesus Christ is Lord. Believers will live with God forever in his kingdom.

Yes!

I have read all the Bible passages.

I have thought about the issues and understand this unit.

Notes:

Notes:

Notes: